C000022673

Compilation copyright © 1990 by Dick Bruna Books, Inc.
Illustrations Dick Bruna, copyright © Mercis bv, 1962, 1963, 1968, 1969, 1972, 1974,
1979, 1980, 1981, 1982, 1984, 1986

Created and manufactured by Dick Bruna Books, Inc., by arrangement with
Ottenheimer Publishers, Inc. Illustrations by Dick Bruna.
No part of this book may be reproduced in any form without written permission from
the publisher.

First published in Great Britain in 1990 by William Collins Sons & Co Ltd,
8 Grafton Street, London W1X 3LA

A CIP catalogue record for this book is available from the British Library

0 00 184581 0

Printed in Italy

I know my shapes

Dick Bruna

COLLINS

circle

A circle is round.

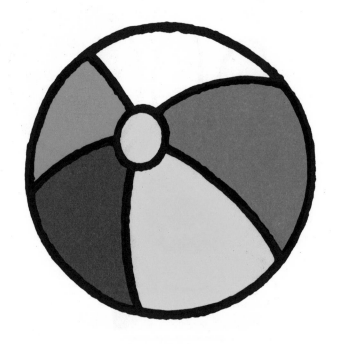

**How many other round objects
can you think of?**

square

A square has four equal sides.

Can you find all the squares here?

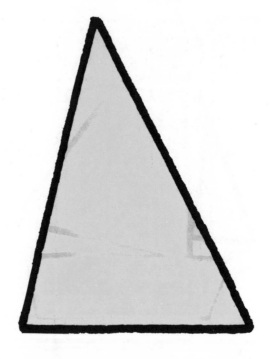

triangle

A triangle has three sides

and three corners.

Lots of things have triangle shapes.

Can you think of others?

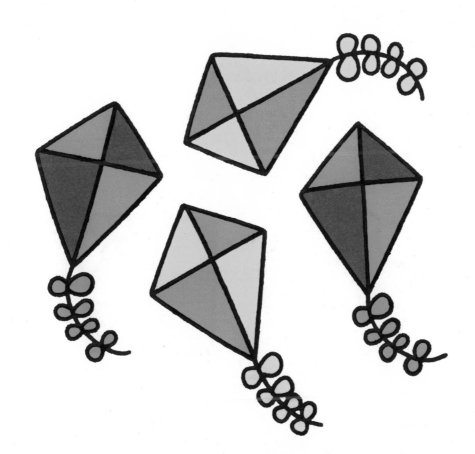

circle, triangle, square.

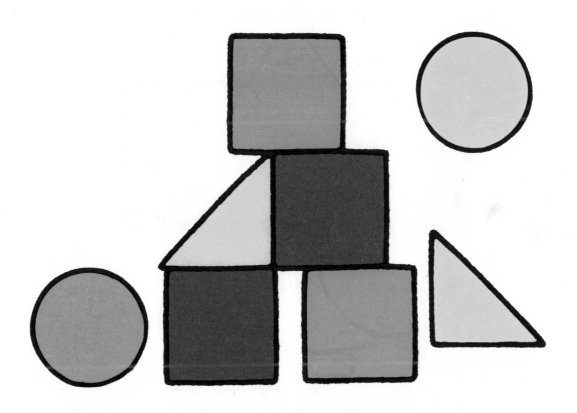

How many shapes can you find here?

rectangle

A rectangle has four corners and four sides,

but is longer than a square.

oval

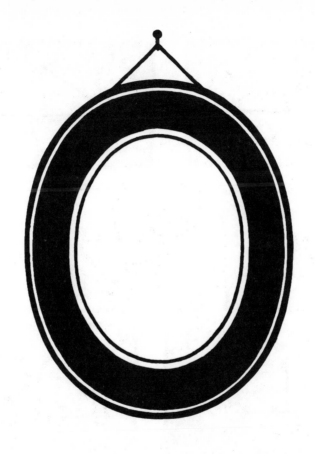

An oval is longer and flatter than a circle.

Which shapes do you see here?

star

A star can have five or six points.

Can you think of other objects with a star shape?

Different shapes are everywhere.

Which ones do you see here?